COLLINS
Mental
Maths 6

Jan Henley

Collins Educational

An imprint of HarperCollins*Publishers*

Rounding to the nearest 10, 100 or 1000

Round these to the nearest 10.

1. 87
2. 348
3. 12 012
4. 34 896
5. 65 995

Round these to the nearest 100.

6. 643
7. 10 521
8. 29 739
9. 78 990
10. 19 962

Round these to the nearest 1000.

11. 4657
12. 23 409
13. 48 721
14. 69 899
15. 99 449

Rounding decimals

Round these to the nearest whole number.

1. 3·2
2. 4·67
3. 12·6
4. 29·32
5. 37·55
6. 129·73
7. 499·51

Round these to the nearest tenth (or to 1 decimal place).

8. 27·82
9. 34·68
10. 12·75
11. 211·94
12. 64·97
13. 477·07
14. 321·11
15. 49·96

Number sequences

Copy and complete the following number sequences and explain each of the rules.

1. 22, 41, 60, 79, ☐, ☐
2. –63, –52, –41, –30, ☐, ☐, ☐
3. 9, 16, 25, ☐, ☐, 64
4. 104, 129, 154, 179, ☐, ☐
5. 98, 83, 68, ☐, 38, ☐
6. 1, 1, 2, 3, 5, 8, 13, ☐, ☐, ☐
7. 10000, 1000, 100, ☐, ☐, 0·1,
8. 0·1, 0·4, 0·7, ☐, ☐, 1·6

9. 1, 3, 6, 10, 15, 21, ☐, ☐
10. 243, 222, 201, ☐, ☐, 138
11. 34, 25, 16, ☐, ☐, ☐
12. 0·27, 0·31, 0·35, 0·39, ☐, ☐
13. 39 600, ☐, 39 800, 39 900, ☐
14. 12·26, 12·41, 12·56, ☐, ☐
15. 63 219, 62 219, 61 219, ☐, ☐

Ordering numbers

Arrange these in order, the least first.

1. –29, 18, 21, –19, –8
2. 19 991, 19 099, 19 091, 19, 199, 19 919,
3. –7, –5, 5, –2, 7, 2

4. 275 000, 225 000, 250 000, 285 000, 205 000
5. 17·71, 71·17, 17·17, 17·7, 71·7
6. 4·56, 5·46, 6·45, 5·64, 4·64

Negative numbers

1. The temperature is –12°C. It rises by 3°C. What is the new temperature?
2. The temperature is –4°C. It rises by 6°C. What is the new temperature?
3. If the temperature is –10°C, by how many degrees must it rise to reach –2°C?
4. The temperature falls from 11°C by day to –5°C at night. By how many degrees does the temperature fall?
5. What is the difference in temperature between –3°C and 13°C?
6. The temperature on Monday is –7°C. It is 2°C warmer on Tuesday. On Wednesday it is 5°C colder than Tuesday. What is Wednesday's temperature?

Squares and cubes

Remember that 3^2 means 3 squared or 3 x 3. $\sqrt{\,}$ 9 means the square root of 9 which is 3. 6 cubed or 6^3 means 6 x 6 x 6 = 216.

What is:

1. 8 squared?
2. $\sqrt{\,}$ 16?
3. The square root of 121?

4. 15^2?
5. $\sqrt{\,}$ 81?
6. $12^2 + 10^2 = \square$

7. 3^3
8. 1000 is $\square$ cubed
9. 9^3

Factors and prime factors

Remember, a factor is a whole number which will divide exactly into another whole number. For example, 1, 2, 4, 8, 16 and 32 are all factors of 32.

Write all the factors of:

1. 24
2. 52
3. 125
4. 99
5. 1000
6. Which of these numbers has an odd number of factors: 12, 25, 37, 42, 64, 69?
7. Which of these numbers has only 2 factors: 5, 17, 27, 49, 57, 61?

A prime factor is a factor which is also a prime number. It cannot be broken down into smaller equal groups. For example, the prime factors of 100 are 2, 3 and 5 as all of the other factors (1, 10, 20, 25, 50 and 100) are not prime numbers.

Write the prime factors of each of these numbers.

8. 21
9. 34
10. 56
11. 67
12. 75
13. 81
14. 89
15. Which number under 100 has the most prime factors?

Multiples

True or false:

1. 63 is a multiple of 7?
2. 72 is a multiple of 3?
3. 90 is a multiple of 4?
4. 87 is a multiple of 3?

5. 74 is a multiple of 6?
6. 102 is a multiple of 8?
7. 230 is a multiple of 20?
8. 350 is a multiple of 7?

The numbers 8 and 12 have three common multiples: 1, 2 and 4.
The highest common multiple of 8 and 12 is 4.

**Find the highest common multiple
of these pairs of numbers.**

9. 12 and 18
10. 30 and 45
11. 6 and 15
12. 18 and 30

13. 25 and 100
14. 75 and 81
15. 24 and 32

CHECK UP 1

1. What is 4 cubed?
2. List all of the factors of 500.
3. Round 79 675 to the nearest thousand.
4. What is the square root of 169?
5. Write all of the odd number multiples of 3 between 30 and 50.
6. List all of the prime factors of 27.
7. Arrange these in order, the largest first:
   29·34, 24·39, 24·93, 23·94, 29·43.

8. What is 10^2?
9. Complete the missing numbers in this sequence:
   175, 154, 133, ☐, 91, ☐
10. Round 39·42 to the nearest whole number.
11. What is the highest common multiple of 36 and 48?
12. What is the difference in temperature between −9°C and 17°C?

Fractions

How many halves altogether are there in:

1. $2\frac{1}{2}$?
2. $7\frac{1}{2}$?
3. $10\frac{1}{2}$?
4. $25\frac{1}{2}$?

How many quarters are there in:

5. $1\frac{1}{2}$?
6. $3\frac{3}{4}$?
7. $9\frac{1}{4}$?
8. $15\frac{1}{2}$?

How many thirds are there in:

9. 2?
10. $5\frac{1}{3}$?
11. $10\frac{2}{3}$?
12. $12\frac{2}{6}$?

Place these in order, the smallest first:

13. $1\frac{3}{4}$, $2\frac{1}{2}$, $1\frac{4}{5}$, $2\frac{2}{3}$, $2\frac{5}{8}$
14. $4\frac{1}{5}$, $5\frac{3}{5}$, $4\frac{1}{2}$, $4\frac{3}{10}$, $5\frac{7}{10}$, $5\frac{1}{2}$

What is:

15. three tenths of 20?
16. $\frac{9}{100}$ of 300?
17. $\frac{3}{5}$ of 40?
18. $\frac{5}{6}$ of 72?
19. $\frac{7}{10}$ of 1000?
20. $\frac{3}{8}$ of 56?

What is:

21. $\frac{11}{100}$ of 500?
22. $\frac{7}{20}$ of 200?
23. $\frac{4}{7}$ of 280?
24. $\frac{5}{9}$ of 72?

What do you need to add to these mixed numbers to make the next whole number?

25. $2\frac{1}{3}$
26. $7\frac{3}{8}$
27. $14\frac{4}{9}$
28. $19\frac{9}{100}$

What number is halfway between:

29. $3\frac{1}{4}$ and $3\frac{1}{2}$?
30. $6\frac{1}{3}$ and $6\frac{2}{3}$?
31. What fraction of £1 is 45p?
32. What fraction of 1 metre is 120 cm?
33. What fraction of 1 kg is 275 g?
34. What is half of one and a half?
35. What is half of one quarter?

Percentages

What is:

1. 50% of 70 m?
2. 10% of £1·50?
3. 25% of 900?
4. 30% of 20 kg?
5. 75% of £2·40?

In a sale, the following reductions were made.
Work out (a) the reduction and (b) the new price.

6. 10% off all items under £20
7. 20% off items between £21 and £30
8. 25% off items over £30

HELP BOX

Value Added Tax (VAT) of 17·5 % is added to the price of many items.
You can calculate 17·5% of an amount by finding 10%, then 5% then 2·5%
using halving methods and then add them together. For example:

17·5% of £50: 10% is £5
5% is £2·50
2·5% is £1·25
Total = £8·25

Work out the VAT on these amounts.

9. £24
10. £18
11. £3·60
12. £120
13. £28·40
14. A netball team win 70% of their 21 matches.
    How many matches do they lose?
15. 40% of the 30 children in Class 6 have school lunch.
    The rest bring packed lunches. How many have school lunch?

Making 10, 100 or 1000

1. $\square$ + 71 = 100
2. 4·8 + $\square$ = 10
3. 674 + $\square$ = 1000
4. 282 + $\square$ = 1000
5. $\square$ + 1·7 = 10
6. 63 + $\square$ = 100
7. $\square$ + 3·4 = 10
8. 45 + $\square$ = 100
9. 368 + $\square$ = 1000
10. 0·8 + $\square$ = 10
11. $\square$ + 111 = 1000
12. 39 + $\square$ = 100
13. 2·2 + $\square$ = 10
14. 17 + $\square$ = 100
15. $\square$ + 944 = 1000

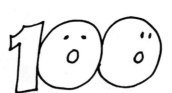

Mixed doubles and halves

1. Double 89
2. 760 + 760 = $\square$
3. Half of 6400
4. 1600 is double $\square$
5. 790 + 790 = $\square$
6. Double 3500
7. 76 + 76 = $\square$
8. 132 is double $\square$
9. 4700 + 4700 = $\square$
10. Half of 96
11. Double 8800
12. Half of 780
13. 540 is double $\square$
14. 1700 + 1700 = $\square$
15. Half of 19 800

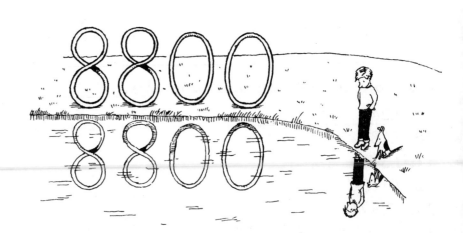

Near doubles

1. 78 + 76 = ☐
2. 1600 + 1500
3. 290 + 270 = ☐
4. 89 + 88 = ☐
5. 550 + 560 = ☐
6. 4900 + 4800 = ☐
7. 7600 + 7700 = ☐
8. 950 + 960 = ☐
9. 27 + 25 = ☐
10. 350 + 370 = ☐
11. 7900 + 7700 = ☐
12. 68 + 69 = ☐
13. 260 + 280 = ☐
14. 99 + 97 = ☐
15. 9900 + 9700 = ☐

HELP BOX

Use your knowledge of doubles to help answer these by identifying near doubles.

CHECK UP 2

1. Double 67
2. 347 + ☐ = 1000
3. What is 25% of 88?
4. 360 + 350 = ☐
5. What is $\frac{4}{7}$ of 210?
6. Half of 3800
7. How many quarters are there in $6\frac{1}{2}$?
8. 6·7 + ☐ = 10
9. 86 + 87 = ☐
10. What is 17·5% of £250?
11. Arrange these in order, the smallest first: $3\frac{3}{4}$, $4\frac{1}{3}$, $3\frac{2}{5}$, $3\frac{9}{10}$.
12. 463 + ☐ = 1000
13. Double 4900
14. A television costing £350 is reduced by 20%. What is its new price?
15. 71 + ☐ = 100

Counting up

Look at the Help Box and try working these out mentally in the same way.

1. 658 + 37 = ☐
2. 346 + 85 = ☐
3. 435 + 73 = ☐
4. 787 + 45 = ☐
5. 486 + 123 = ☐
6. 528 + 291 = ☐
7. 257 + 74 = ☐

HELP BOX

Try these by counting up through
the next multiple of 10.
For example: 347 + 28 = (347 + 3) + (28 − 3)
= 350 + 25
= 375

When subtracting, try starting with the
smaller number and counting up through
the next multiple of 10, 100 or 1000.

For example:
5000 − 2438 = 2 + 60 + 500 + 2000

= 2562

8. 4000 − 1376 = ☐
9. 6000 − 3681 = ☐
10. 7000 − 2035 = ☐
11. 3000 − 1204 = ☐
12. 9000 − 4628 = ☐
13. 2000 − 437 = ☐
14. 8000 − 2316 = ☐
15. 5000 − 3362 = ☐

Partitioning

HELP BOX

This time, work these out mentally by breaking the numbers into hundreds,
tens and ones. For example: 453 + 228 = 681 because 400 + 200 = 600,
50 + 20 = 70 and 3 + 8 = 11 = 600 + 70 + 11
or 453 + 200 + 20 + 8 = 653 + 20 + 8 = 673 + 8 = 681

1. 346 + 129 = ☐
2. 567 + 264 = ☐
3. 532 + 286 = ☐
4. 419 + 367 = ☐
5. 745 + 188 = ☐
6. 386 + 55 = ☐
7. 644 + 207 = ☐

Try these subtraction
questions in a similar way.
For example:
637 − 58 = 637 − 50 − 8
= 587 − 8
= 579

8. 436 − 65 = ☐
9. 281 − 38 = ☐
10. 762 − 143 = ☐
11. 816 − 234 = ☐
12. 523 − 48 = ☐
13. 927 − 365 = ☐
14. 377 + 139 = ☐
15. 624 − 208 = ☐

Adding several two-digit numbers

1. $28 + 35 + 42 = \square$
2. $54 + 49 + 52 + 51 = \square$
3. $63 + 28 + \square = 118$
4. $17 + 81 + 28 + \square = 148$
5. $38 + 96 + 51 + 15 = \square$
6. $19 + 29 + 49 = \square$
7. $23 + \square + 25 + 24 = 94$
8. $47 + 36 + 43 + 29 = \square$
9. $36 + 37 + 15 = \square$
10. $53 + 28 + 32 = \square$
11. $71 + 73 + 74 + 72 = \square$
12. $27 + 21 + \square = 146$
13. $36 + \square + 54 + 12 = 120$
14. $78 + 32 + \square + 15 = 165$
15. $38 + 43 + 42 + 44 = \square$

Write about the strategies you used.

HELP BOX

Don't forget to use different strategies to help you. For example, start with the largest number and look for pairs that make multiples of 10. You could also look for sequences like this:

$$63 + 67 + 61 = (60 \times 3) + (3 + 7 + 1)$$
$$= 180 + 11$$
$$= 191$$

Adding several three-digit numbers

Explain the strategies you use to work out these sums.

1. $370 + 250 + 130 = \square$
2. $460 + 450 + 470 = \square$
3. $480 + \square + 260 = 880$
4. $\square + 290 + 370 = 970$
5. $320 + 110 + 440 + 130 = \square$
6. $350 + 370 + \square = 900$
7. $490 + \square + 310 = 950$
8. $520 + 350 + \square = 1100$
9. $680 + \square + 310 = 1150$
10. $750 + 740 + 730 = \square$
11. $160 + 560 + 360 = \square$
12. $\square + 630 + 620 = 1880$
13. $230 + \square + 450 + 750 = 1600$
14. $920 + \square + 280 = 2050$
15. $860 + 530 + 540 = \square$

Adding and subtracting four-digit multiples of 100

1. 2600 + 4700 = ☐
2. 7200 + 1900 = ☐
3. ☐ + 3800 = 6500
4. 5400 + ☐ = 9200
5. 7200 – 3400 = ☐
6. 8800 – 2900 = ☐
7. 4700 – ☐ = 1800
8. ☐ – 3500 = 4600

9. 3800 + 4900 = ☐
10. 6600 + 2700 = ☐
11. ☐ + 3700 = 8100
12. 6200 – 5500 = ☐
13. 9100 – 7300 = ☐
14. ☐ – 5100 = 2900
15. 8400 – ☐ = 3800

Adding and subtracting three-digit multiples of 10

Explain the strategies you use to answer these.

1. 567 + 350 = ☐
2. 438 + ☐ = 608
3. 1135 – 360 = ☐
4. ☐ – 470 = 542
5. 751 – ☐ = 280
6. 941 – 690 = ☐
7. 1233 – 970 = ☐
8. 486 + 750 = ☐
9. ☐ + 370 = 842
10. 613 + ☐ = 900
11. 424 – 180 = ☐
12. ☐ – 770 = 428
13. 882 – 591 = ☐
14. 477 + 570 = ☐
15. ☐ – 290 = 8331

Related facts – whole numbers

HELP BOX

Remember, if you know that 2020 – 1895 = 125, you also know that:
1895 + 125 = 2020; 125 + 1895 = 2020 and 2020 – 125 = 1895

Work out the answer to each of these questions and then write 3 other related addition and subtraction facts.

1. 3480 + 1230 = ☐
2. 4420 – 2870 = ☐
3. 1250 + 4680 = ☐
4. 9840 – 7360 = ☐
5. 6710 – 3430 = ☐
6. 5000 – 1240 = ☐
7. 5550 + 750 = ☐
8. 3680 + 2570 = ☐
9. 4200 – 2950 = ☐
10. 7420 + 1870 = ☐

Write 4 different addition and subtraction sentences about each set of 3 numbers:

11. 5600, 1800, 3800
12. 3750, 1860, 1890
13. 3200, 3210, 6410
14. 4350, 3560, 7910

15. Use these numbers to write as many different addition or subtraction sentences as you can: 4680, 3920, 7520, 1290, 6430.

CHECK UP 3

Practise using the strategies you have learnt when answering these. Explain the methods you used.

1. 5000 – 2319 = ☐
2. 56 + 27 = ☐
3. 3400 – 1800 = ☐
4. 431 – 270 = ☐
5. 17 + 19 + 18 + 16 = ☐
6. 68 + 25 = ☐
7. 340 + ☐ + 260 = 890
8. 726 + 157 = ☐
9. 4100 – ☐ = 2700
10. 7000 – ☐ = 4567
11. 674 + 158 = ☐
12. 27 + 47 + 37 + 17 = ☐
13. 613 – 350 = ☐
14. 3800 + 4600 = ☐
15. 832 + ☐ = 941

To the next tenth or whole number

1. $3.46 + \boxed{} = 4$
2. $5.73 + \boxed{} = 5.8$
3. $6.81 + \boxed{} = 6.9$
4. $1.33 + \boxed{} = 2$
5. $8.04 + \boxed{} = 8.1$
6. $6.29 + \boxed{} = 6.3$
7. $4.11 + \boxed{} = 5$
8. $2.04 + \boxed{} = 3$

9. $8.59 + \boxed{} = 9$
10. $3.22 + \boxed{} = 3.3$
11. $0.34 + \boxed{} = 1$
12. $9.51 + \boxed{} = 10$
13. $7.63 + \boxed{} = 7.7$
14. $1.78 + \boxed{} = 1.8$
15. $4.54 + \boxed{} = 5$

Adding and subtracting decimals less than 1

1. $0.36 + 0.5 = \boxed{}$
2. $0.4 + 0.21 = \boxed{}$
3. $0.7 - 0.39 = \boxed{}$
4. $0.56 - \boxed{} = 0.26$
5. $\boxed{} + 0.4 = 0.92$
6. $0.33 + \boxed{} = 0.53$
7. $0.04 + 0.7 = \boxed{}$
8. $0.6 - \boxed{} = 0.29$
9. $0.89 - 0.6 = \boxed{}$
10. $0.75 + \boxed{} = 0.95$
11. $0.3 - 0.02 = \boxed{}$
12. $\boxed{} + 0.19 = 0.59$
13. $\boxed{} + 0.7 = 0.71$
14. $0.21 - 0.1 = \boxed{}$
15. $\boxed{} - 0.67 = 0.13$

Adding and subtracting decimals more than 1

1. $5.32 + 4.4 = \square$
2. $12.71 + 6.19 = \square$
3. $7.89 - 5.2 = \square$
4. $9.43 - 6.02 = \square$
5. $15.35 + \square = 18.86$
6. $11.57 - 9.33 = \square$
7. $3.91 + 5.75 = \square$
8. $\square + 2.83 = 6.43$

9. $20.11 - 10.08 = \square$
10. $17.67 - \square = 5.99$
11. $\square - 3.29 = 4.81$
12. $45.62 + \square = 60$
13. $27.14 - 2.55 = \square$
14. $20.2 - 7.68 = \square$
15. $11.75 + \square = 22.89$

Related facts – decimals

HELP BOX

Remember, if you know that $10.11 - 1.21 = 8.9$ you also know that:
$1.21 + 8.9 = 10.11$; $8.9 + 1.21 = 10.11$; $10.11 - 8.9 = 1.21$

Work out the answer to these questions and write 3 other addition or subtraction sentences about each set of numbers.

1. $5.2 + 3.89 = \square$
2. $7.43 - 2.51 = \square$
3. $5.4 - 2.12 = \square$
4. $12.34 + 15.58 = \square$
5. $13.81 - 5.9 = \square$
6. $6.29 + 3.81 = \square$
7. $31.22 - 27.99 = \square$
8. $9.75 + 8.95 = \square$
9. $12.32 - 9.4 = \square$
10. $36.36 + 24.24 = \square$

Write 4 different addition or subtraction sentences about each of these sets of numbers.

11. $2.31, 3.22, 0.91$
12. $7.56, 7.6, 15.16$
13. $12.64, 6.31, 6.33$
14. $19.24, 37.51, 18.27$
15. $7.35, 15, 7.65$

Decimal problems

1. What is the difference between 4·7 and 6·5?
2. What must I add to 7·6 to make 8·2?
3. How many more than 34·3 is 41·8?
4. What must I take from 11·2 to leave 9·8?
5. 12·7 add a number is 19·3. What is the number?
6. Subtract 3·5 from 10·2
7. Decrease 15·6 by 4·9
8. What number when added to 45·8 makes 50·3?
9. What is the difference between 19·6 and 8·8?
10. What must I add to 22·7 to make 33·1?
11. How many less than 8·3 is 5·7?
12. Decrease 17·5 by 6·7
13. What must I take from 56·4 to leave 49·8?
14. What is 16·4 more than 12·9?
15. Find 3 pairs of numbers with a difference of 11·6.

CHECK UP 4

1. 4·37 + ☐ = 4·4
2. 0·6 + 0·35 = ☐
3. 0·7 − 0·07 = ☐
4. How many less is 5·2 than 7·1?
5. What must I add to 23·31 to make 25·55?
6. 8·63 − 4·35 = ☐
7. 6·7 + ☐ = 7

8. Decrease 17·21 by 0·5
9. 0·8 − ☐ = 0·66
10. 9·91 + ☐ = 10
11. 5·8 + 0·07 = ☐
12. What is 19·7 more than 15·3?
13. 9·49 − 6·7 = ☐
14. 0·4 − 0·32 = ☐
15. 45·2 + ☐ = 50

Tables facts

1. 8 x 6 = ☐
2. How many 7s in 63?
3. 54 ÷ 6 = ☐
4. Nine threes
5. Divide 24 by 6
6. 7 x 8 = ☐
7. 81 ÷ 9 = ☐
8. 4 multiplied by 9
9. 5 x ☐ = 40
10. Six sevens
11. 9 x 8 = ☐
12. How many 9s in 45?
13. What is the product of 5 and 8?
14. 72 divided by 9
15. 7 x 4 = ☐

More doubles and halves

1. $\frac{1}{2}$ of 96
2. Twice 350
3. Double 42 $\frac{1}{2}$
4. 8900 x 2 = ☐
5. 3500 ÷ 2 = ☐
6. Half of 59
7. 470 over 2 = ☐
8. Double 39
9. $\frac{1}{2}$ of 7300
10. 1250 x 2 = ☐
11. Twice 26 $\frac{1}{2}$
12. 97 over 2 = ☐
13. 475 is half of ☐
14. 610 ÷ 2 = ☐
15. Half of 1100

Doubling

1. Double 173
2. 439 x 2
3. Twice 189
4. 377 x 2 = ☐
5. Double 186
6. Twice 357
7. 476 x 2 = ☐
8. Double 358
9. 382 x 2 = ☐
10. 166 x 2 = ☐
11. 238 x 2 = ☐
12. Double 376
13. Twice 419
14. 338 x 2 = ☐
15. Double 179

Work these out by doubling the hundreds first, then the tens and finally the units.

For example: double 264 = 400 + 120 + 8

= 528

Double then halve

HELP
BOX

1. 23 x 5 = ☐
2. 7 x 15 = ☐
3. 9 x 35 = ☐
4. 32 x 5 = ☐
5. 8 x 45 = ☐
6. 14 x 15 = ☐
7. 18 x 35 = ☐
8. 56 x 5 = ☐
9. 16 x 15 = ☐
10. 45 x 9 = ☐
11. 89 x 5 = ☐
12. 22 x 15 = ☐
13. 7 x 35 = ☐
14. 5 x 73 = ☐
15. 97 x 5 = ☐

Work out these multiplication questions by doubling one of the numbers in the calculation and then halving the result.

For example:
$19 \times 5 = 95$ because it is $(19 \times 10) \div 2 = 190 \div 2 = 95$.

Halve then double

HELP BOX

1. 20 x 12 = ☐
2. 17 x 8 = ☐
3. 14 x 7 = ☐
4. 13 x 14 = ☐
5. 26 x 20 = ☐
6. 32 x 8 = ☐
7. 6 x 18 = ☐
8. 14 x 9 = ☐
9. 8 x 16 = ☐
10. 11 x 12 = ☐
11. 38 x 20 = ☐
12. 32 x 8 = ☐
13. 16 x 11 = ☐
14. 21 x 14 = ☐
15. 6 x 16 = ☐

Work these out by halving one of the numbers and then doubling the result.

For example: 14 x 8 = (14 x 4) x 2

$$= 56 \times 2$$
$$= 112$$

Multiplying by 15

HELP BOX

1. 12 x 15 = ☐
2. 21 x 15 = ☐
3. 9 x 15 = ☐
4. 17 x 15 = ☐
5. 32 x 15 = ☐
6. 24 x 15 = ☐
7. 18 x 15 = ☐
8. 27 x 15 = ☐
9. 41 x 15 = ☐
10. 11 x 15 = ☐
11. 25 x 15 = ☐
12. 36 x 15 = ☐
13. 29 x 15 = ☐
14. 30 x 15 = ☐
15. 35 x 15 = ☐

To multiply a number by 15, start by multiplying it by 10, halve the result, then add the two answers together.

For example: 16 x 15 = 240 because

$$16 \times 10 = 160$$
$$160 \div 2 = 80$$
$$160 + 80 = 240$$

Multiplying by 25

HELP BOX

To multiply by 25, first multiply by 100 and then divide the result by 4.
For example: 28 x 25 = 700 because 28 x 100 = 2800 and 2800 ÷ 4 = 700

1. 16 x 25 = ☐
2. 32 x 25 = ☐
3. 44 x 25 = ☐
4. 18 x 25 = ☐
5. 22 x 25 = ☐
6. 34 x 25 = ☐
7. 31 x 25 = ☐
8. 19 x 25 = ☐

9. 21 x 25 = ☐
10. 35 x 25 = ☐
11. 41 x 25 = ☐
12. 39 x 25 = ☐
13. 17 x 25 = ☐
14. 36 x 25 = ☐
15. 82 x 25 = ☐

Doubling tables facts

**Decide which tables facts you could double
to answer these multiplication questions.**

1. 6 x 18 = ☐
2. 8 x 14 = ☐
3. 9 x 12 = ☐
4. 7 x 18 = ☐
5. 6 x 14 = ☐
6. 4 x 18 = ☐
7. 7 x 16 = ☐
8. 7 x 12 = ☐
9. 9 x 18 = ☐
10. 9 x 16 = ☐
11. 8 x 18 = ☐
12. 9 x 14 = ☐
13. 6 x 16 = ☐
14. 7 x 14 = ☐
15. 8 x 16 = ☐

HELP BOX

You can work out the 14 times table
by doubling the 7 times table facts.

The 24 times table

HELP
BOX

1. 3 x 24 = ☐   **5.** 8 x 24 = ☐
2. 7 x 24 = ☐   **6.** 4 x 24 = ☐
3. 9 x 24 = ☐   **7.** 6 x 24 = ☐
4. 5 x 24 = ☐

> You can work out the 24 times table facts by doubling and doubling again the facts you know from the 6 times table.

Double then double again

HELP
BOX

> Look at the doubling pattern to help you to complete these multiplication statements.

1. 1 x 24 = ☐
   2 x 24 = ☐
   4 x 24 = ☐
   8 x 24 = ☐
   ☐ x 24 = 192

2. 1 x 32 = ☐
   2 x 32 = ☐
   4 x 32 = ☐
   8 x 32 = ☐
   ☐ x 32 = 256

Try to continue the sequence as far as possible using mental strategies.

Finding fractions by halving

HELP
BOX

> You can find a sixth of a number by finding a third and then halving the number. Twelfths can be worked out by halving sixths. For example: $\frac{1}{12}$ of 300 is 25 because: $\frac{1}{3}$ of 300 is 100, $\frac{1}{6}$ of 300 is 50, so $\frac{1}{12}$ is half of 50.

Find these fractions by using a halving strategy.

1. One sixth of 300
2. $\frac{1}{20}$ of 700
3. One twelfth of 600
4. $\frac{1}{40}$ of 200
5. $\frac{1}{12}$ of 900
6. One twentieth of 1300
7. $\frac{1}{6}$ of 450
8. $\frac{1}{4}$ of £3000

9. $\frac{1}{40}$ of 3000
10. $\frac{1}{6}$ of 1·5 m
11. One sixth of 1500
12. $\frac{1}{18}$ of 450
13. One fourteenth of 210
14. One sixteenth of 240
15. $\frac{1}{18}$ of 9000

All of these questions use doubling and halving strategies.
Try to practise the different strategies you have learnt.

1. 87 x 2 = ☐
2. Double 47 $\frac{1}{2}$
3. 14 x 15 = ☐
4. Double 178
5. 29 x 25 = ☐
6. $\frac{1}{12}$ of 60
7. 18 x 15 = ☐
8. 6 x 35 = ☐

9. 17 x 14 = ☐
10. 355 x 2 = ☐
11. Half of 97
12. 33 x 25 = ☐
13. 6 x 45 = ☐
14. $\frac{1}{20}$ of 700
15. 47 x 25 = ☐

Using factors

Look at the Help Box. Now try to use factors to work out these.

1. 378 ÷ 14
2. 27 x 21 = ☐
3. 41 x 18 = ☐
4. 352 ÷ 16 = ☐
5. 22 x 18 = ☐
6. 315 ÷ 21 = ☐
7. 17 x 14 = ☐
8. 231 ÷ 9 = ☐
9. 19 x 16 = ☐
10. 17 x 24 = ☐
11. 336 ÷ 16 = ☐
12. 23 x 18 = ☐

HELP BOX

Use your knowledge of factors to help with multiplication and division. For example, for the sum 23 x 21, two of the factors of 21 are 7 and 3 so:

23 x 7 = 161

161 x 3 = 483 so 23 x 21 = 483.

414 ÷ 18 use these factors of 18, 6 and 3

414 ÷ 3 = 138

138 ÷ 6 = 23 so 414 ÷ 18 = 23

The 17 times table

1. 4 x 17 = ☐
2. 7 x 17 = ☐
3. 3 x 17 = ☐
4. 9 x 17 = ☐
5. 6 x 17 = ☐
6. 8 x 17 = ☐
7. 5 x 17 = ☐

HELP BOX

Work out these multiplication facts by adding together the 10 times table facts and the 7 times table facts.

Multiplying and dividing by 10, 100 and 1000

1. 53 x 100 = ☐
2. 15 x 1000 = ☐
3. ☐ x 10 = 5000
4. 20 x ☐ = 20 000
5. $\frac{1}{100}$ of 6500
6. How many times larger is 3500 than 350?
7. 340 ÷ 10 = ☐
8. How many £100 notes are there in £12 000?
9. 12 x ☐ = 12 000
10. How many times smaller is 360 than 36 000?
11. How many 10p coins are there in £42.50?
12. 3400 ÷ 10 = ☐
13. 4900 ÷ ☐ = 49
14. 27 x 1000 = ☐
15. 44 x ☐ = 440
16. $\frac{1}{1000}$ of 60 000
17. How many centimetres are there in 20 metres?
18. One hundredth of 520
19. 512 x 100 = ☐
20. ☐ x 100 = 3500

HELP BOX

Remember that when *multiplying* by 10, 100 or 1000 the digits move 1, 2 or 3 places to the left. When *dividing* by 10, 100 or 1000 the digits move to the right.

Multiplying by 49 or 51

1. 18 x 51 = ☐
2. 24 x 49 = ☐
3. 21 x 51 = ☐
4. 32 x 49 = ☐
5. 41 x 49 = ☐
6. 19 x 51 = ☐
7. 27 x 51 = ☐
8. 31 x 49 = ☐
9. 16 x 51 = ☐
10. 35 x 49 = ☐
11. 53 x 51 = ☐
12. 64 x 49 = ☐
13. 71 x 51 = ☐
14. 75 x 49 = ☐
15. 83 x 49 = ☐

HELP BOX

To multiply a number by 49 or 51, multiply by 50 first and then add or subtract the number.

For example: 16 x 49 = 784 because it is
(16 x 50) – 16
800 – 16 = 784

Multiplying by 99 and 101

HELP BOX

Work these out by multiplying by 100 and then adding or subtracting the number you multiplied by 100.

1. 14 x 99 = ☐
2. 24 x 101 = ☐
3. 32 x 99 = ☐
4. 38 x 101 = ☐
5. 21 x 99 = ☐
6. 33 x 101 = ☐
7. 46 x 99 = ☐
8. 49 x 101 = ☐

9. 37 x 101 = ☐
10. 43 x 99 = ☐
11. 52 x 101 = ☐
12. 55 x 99 = ☐
13. 63 x 99 = ☐
14. 72 x 101 = ☐
15. 79 x 99 = ☐

Multiplying two-digit numbers by a single digit

HELP BOX

Try these by multiplying the tens first and then the ones. For example:

$$74 \times 8 = (70 \times 8) + (4 \times 8)$$
$$= 560 + 32$$
$$= 592$$

1. 36 x 7 = ☐

2. 43 x 6 = ☐

3. 47 x 8 = ☐

4. 57 x 9 = ☐

5. 66 x 6 = ☐

6. 73 x 8 = ☐

7. 58 x 7 = ☐

8. 78 x 9 = ☐

9. 47 x 8 = ☐

10. 83 x 6 = ☐

11. 69 x 7 = ☐

12. 85 x 7 = ☐

13. 91 x 8 = ☐

14. 77 x 6 = ☐

15. 68 x 8 = ☐

CHECK UP 6

1. 23 x 99 = ☐

2. 67 x 6 = ☐

3. 35 x ☐ = 3500

4. 9 x 17 = ☐

5. 31 x 49 = ☐

6. 410 ÷ ☐ = 41

7. 78 x 6 = ☐

8. 56 x 1000 = ☐

9. How many times larger is 3600 than 360?

10. 43 x 101 = ☐

11. 7 x 17 = ☐

12. Divide 7900 by 100

13. 28 x 51 = ☐

14. 58 x 7 = ☐

15. 67 x 99 = ☐

Multiplying decimals less than 1

1. $0.6 \times 4 = \square$
2. $0.7 \times 3 = \square$
3. $0.8 \times \square = 6.4$
4. $0.5 \times 9 = \square$
5. $0.9 \times \square = 7.2$
6. $\square \times 8 = 5.6$
7. $0.9 \times \square = 5.4$
8. $0.7 \times 6 = \square$

9. $0.8 \times 4 = \square$
10. $\square \times 7 = 4.2$
11. $0.8 \times \square = 2.4$
12. $0.4 \times 6 = \square$
13. $\square \times 7 = 0.7$
14. $0.2 \times \square = 1.8$
15. $0.7 \times 5 = \square$

Multiplying units and tenths by a single digit

1. $7.2 \times 4 = \square$
2. $4.8 \times 6 = \square$
3. $5.4 \times 5 = \square$
4. $5.7 \times 7 = \square$
5. $3.9 \times 8 = \square$
6. $6.4 \times 9 = \square$
7. $7.3 \times 8 = \square$
8. $9.1 \times 7 = \square$
9. $8.8 \times 6 = \square$
10. $7.6 \times 5 = \square$
11. $8.5 \times 4 = \square$
12. $6.7 \times 7 = \square$
13. $4.6 \times 8 = \square$
14. $5.3 \times 9 = \square$
15. $6.8 \times 8 = \square$

HELP BOX

Multiply the ones or units first then the tenths.

For example:
$$8.3 \times 6 = (8 \times 6) + (0.3 \times 6)$$
$$= 48 + 1.8$$
$$= 49.8$$

Multiplying decimals by 10

1. 3·34 x 10 = ☐
2. 4·15 times 10 = ☐
3. £5·22 x 10 = ☐
4. 5·09 x 10 = ☐
5. £6·80 x 10 = ☐
6. 7·31 x 10 = ☐
7. What is the product of 3·55 and 10?
8. 5·9 multiplied by 10 = ☐
9. 4·33 m x 10 = ☐
10. 8·01 x 10 = ☐
11. 7·1 kg x 10 = ☐
12. 1·01 x 10 = ☐
13. 6·92 multiplied by 10
14. 2·07 m x 10 = ☐
15. 9·89 x 10 = ☐

Multiplying decimals by 100

1. 6·1 x 100 = ☐
2. 3·8 x 100 = ☐
3. £5·10 x 100 = ☐
4. 8·9 multiplied by 100
5. 3·7 cm x 100
6. 1·3 x 100 = ☐
7. 6·9 x 100 = ☐
8. 4·2 times 100
9. £7·99 x 100 = ☐
10. 3·4 cm x 100 = ☐
11. 7·4 multiplied by 100
12. What is the product of 3·8 and 100?
13. ☐ x 100 = £290
14. 9·7 x 100 = ☐
15. 8·6 times 100

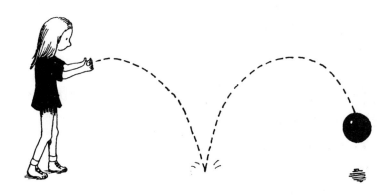

Dividing decimals by 10 and 100

1. $32 \div 100 = \square$
2. $\frac{1}{10}$ of 45
3. $\square \div 10 = 0.9$
4. $8 \div 100 = \square$
5. One hundredth of £55
6. $\square \div 100 = 0.4$
7. 43 divided by 100
8. $8 \div \square = 0.08$

9. $76 \div \square = 7.6$
10. One tenth of 7
11. $\frac{1}{100}$ of 40
12. 9 divided by 100
13. $\square \div 100 = 0.63$
14. $72 \div \square = 7.2$
15. $54 \div \square = 0.54$

More related facts – decimals

HELP BOX

> Remember, if you know that
> $0.35 \times 5 = 1.75$ you also know that:
> $5 \times 0.35 = 1.75$, $1.75 \div 0.35 = 5$
> and $1.75 \div 5 = 0.35$

Look at this sum and work out the following.

$2.3 \times 1.2 = 2.76$

1. $1.2 \times 2.3 = \square$
2. $2.76 \div 1.2 = \square$
3. $2.76 \div \square = 1.2$

Look at this sum and work out the following.

$51.6 \div 12 = 4.3$

4. $4.3 \times 12 = \square$
5. $51.6 \div \square = 12$
6. $\square \times 4.3 = 51.6$

Work out the answer then write 3 other multiplication or division sentences.

7. $2.5 \times 6 = \square$
8. $1.24 \div 2 = \square$
9. $0.5 \div 2 = \square$
10. $1.23 \times 3 = \square$
11. $0.7 \times 5 = \square$
12. Use 0.2, 0.4 and 0.08 to write 4 different multiplication or division facts relating to these numbers.

Doubling decimals

1. 0·7 x 2 = ☐
2. 0·23 x 2 = ☐
3. Double 0·7
4. Twice 0·04
5. 0·19 x 2 = ☐
6. 0·65 x 2 = ☐
7. ☐ x 2 = 1·8
8. 0·59 x 2 = ☐
9. Double 0·67
10. ☐ x 2 = 1·22
11. 0·09 x 2 = ☐
12. 0·6 x 2 = ☐
13. ☐ x 2 = 1·3
14. Double 0·98
15. ☐ x 2 = 1·74

Halving decimals

1. 0·4 ÷ 2 = ☐
2. Half of 0·68
3. 0·76 ÷ 2 = ☐
4. $\frac{1}{2}$ of 0·52
5. ☐ ÷ 2 = 0·17
6. Half of 0·16
7. $\frac{1}{2}$ of 0·8
8. ☐ ÷ 2 = 0·39
9. ☐ ÷ 2 = 0·3
10. 0·25 ÷ 2 = ☐
11. Half of 0·3
12. $\frac{1}{2}$ of 0·63
13. 0·98 ÷ 2 = ☐
14. 0·71 ÷ 2 = ☐
15. $\frac{1}{2}$ of 0·03

CHECK UP 7

1. 4·7 x 4 = ☐
2. 0·5 x 100 = ☐
3. ½ of 0·09
4. Double 0·65
5. 6·05 x 10
6. ☐ x 7 = 6·3
7. 3·9 x ☐ = 390
8. Half of 0·72

9. 8·56 x ☐ = 85·6
10. Double 0·89
11. 43 ÷ 10 = ☐
12. 560 ÷ ☐ = 5·6
13. 3·8 x 5 = ☐
14. 0·34 ÷ 2 = ☐
15. 331 ÷ 100 = ☐

What operation?

Decide what operation sign goes in each box.
Write the whole question in your book.

1. 345 ☐ 245 = 590
2. 450 ☐ 10 = 4500
3. 475 ☐ 25 = 19
4. 17 ☐ 3 ☐ 10 = 24
5. 107 ☐ 25 = 4·28
6. 127 ☐ 309 = −182
7. 36 ☐ 4 ☐ 7 = 63
8. (18 ☐ 34) ☐ 2 = 26
9. 17 ☐ (15 ☐ 5) = 14
10. 362 ☐ 28 = 10 136
11. 47 ☐ 24 ☐ 4 = 92
12. (96 ☐ 32) ☐ 49 = 52
13. 759 ☐ 25 = 30·36
14. 35 ☐ 3 ☐ 20 = 85
15. (12 ☐ 4) ☐ 14 = 112

Money

Work out the cost of:

1. 3 daffodil bulbs
2. 2 hyacinth bulbs
3. 10 crocuses

What is the total cost of:

8. £1·99, £12·50 and £110
9. £175, £32·10 and £4·50

In a half-price sale work out the new price labels:

4. £133
5. £19·98
6. £1·76
7. £1550

Menu

Cola 30p
Milkshake 95p
Fries 59p
Burger ...... £1·25
Fish .... £1·40

10. What is the price of a cola, burger and fries?
11. How much change from £5 would you get if you bought a portion of fish, fries and a milkshake?
12. How much would it cost for 4 people to have burger and fries?

Time

How many:

1. days in 47 weeks?
2. hours in 17 days?
3. seconds in 51 minutes?
4. days in 5 years?
5. years in 12 centuries?

What is the total number of days in:

6. January, March and June?
7. February in a leap year, October, May and December?
8. A train travels at 125 miles per hour. How far will it travel in 3 hours?

9. A walker sets off at 9 a.m. and walks at a speed of 6 km per hour. If he takes no breaks how far will he have walked at 12:30 p.m.?
10. A television programme is shown every weekday for 25 minutes. How long is it on air each week?

Work out the difference between these pairs of times.

11. 01:17   09:56
12. 08:27   12:04
13. 11:46   16:21
14. 10:25   21:09
15. 22:35   00:14

Measures

How many:

1. metres in 4·5 kilometres?
2. grams in 13 kilograms?
3. millimetres in 7 metres?
4. centimetres in 2·37 metres?
5. decimetres in 2 kilometres?
6. millilitres in 0·05 litres?

Use the information showing the approximate imperial value of some metric quantities to answer these questions:

7. How many ounces (oz) in 150 grams?
8. How many kilometres in 30 miles?
9. How many pounds (lb) in 0·5 kg?
10. How many millilitres in 2 ½ pints?
11. Write 30 mm in metres.
12. Write 600 grams in kilograms.
13. Write 340 millilitres in litres.

Metric	Imperial
1 kilogram	2 lb
30 grams	1 oz
1 litre	2 pints
8 kilometres	5 miles

Find the total length of:

14. 1·23 m, 0·47 m and 134 cm
15. 3·5 km, 4550 m, 5·75 km and 200 m